ALL WEATHER TRAINING
TRAINING
beating the elements

ALL WEATHER TRAINING
beating the elements

© Peak Performance Publishing 2005

A CIP catalogue record for this book is available from the British Library.

Printed by: Baskerville Press Ltd
6-8 Newton Road, Salisbury, Wiltshire SP2 7QB

Published by Peak Performance Publishing

Peak Performance Publishing is a trading name of Electric Word plc
Registered office: 67-71 Goswell Road, London, EC1V 7EP
Tel: 0845 450 6402
Registered number: 3934419

ISBN: 1-905096-09-7

Publisher Jonathan A. Pye
Editor Isabel Walker
Designer The Flying Fish Studios Ltd

OTHER TITLES IN THE PEAK PERFORMANCE SPECIAL REPORT SERIES

ACHILLES TENDINITIS –
PREVENTION AND TREATMENT

CARBO LOADING –
FOR THAT EXTRA EDGE

COACHING YOUNG ATHLETES

CREATINE –
CUTTING THROUGH THE MYTHS

DYNAMIC STRENGTH TRAINING FOR SWIMMERS

TRAINING FOR MASTER ATHLETES

FEMALE ATHLETES –
TRAINING FOR SUCCESS

SHOULDER INJURIES –
PREVENTION AND TREATMENT

MARATHON TRAINING –
FOR YOUR PERSONAL BEST

NUTRITIONAL SUPPLEMENTS –
BOOSTING YOUR PERFORMANCE

SPORTS PSYCHOLOGY –
THE WILL TO WIN

TRAINING FOR SPEED, POWER & STRENGTH

CONTENTS

From the editor

Peak athletic performance is not just about getting the most out of your body; it is also about anticipating and meeting the various challenges thrown at you by different environmental conditions, including hot and cold climates, altitudinous terrain and polluted cities. And it is about preparing yourself to be at your best at different times of the day and in far-flung time zones.

All these issues and more are covered in this special report on all-weather training, prepared for you by PP's expert team of regular writers. We start with a comprehensive pre-competition strategy for staying cool in the heat, move on to consider the various techniques for pre-cooling (useful in winter as well as summer!), then go on to look at the impact of pollution on performance.

Next, altitude training: does it really aid sea-level performance or is it a rather expensive waste of time? On to the problems of working out in the cold – and you might be surprised to learn that dehydration can be as much – if not more – of a problem in freezing conditions than in the heat. Which brings us neatly to our final two articles on the core issue of fluid balance, the first weighing up the pros and cons of sports drinks as compared with plain water, and the second helping you to calculate your individual fluid needs (yes, they really do vary widely) and devise your personal hydration plan.

I hope you enjoy this special report and find it useful all year round.

Isabel Walker

Isabel Walker
Editor

Your pre-competition strategy for staying cool when the heat is on

Sustained hard exercise in a hot environment presents a greater challenge to the body's homoeostatic mechanisms than any other situation. The combination of a high rate of metabolic heat production and a restricted capacity for heat dissipation leads to hyperthermia (high body temperature), which may progress to heat illness, inevitably impairing exercise performance.

It has been demonstrated, in sports science labs, that prolonged cycling capacity is lower at 21°C than at 11°C and is even further reduced at 31°C, when VO_2max is reduced, heart rate increased and skin and rectal temperature elevated [1]. Heart rate rises in an attempt to meet increasing pressures on the blood supply, to increase skin blood flow for cooling purposes and to maintain oxygen supply to the working muscles.

Heat exposure combined with exercise results not just in hyperthermia but also in hypohydration (low fluid levels) if fluid losses are not replaced, and this combination will dramatically reduce exercise capacity. There may be a critical core temperature that is the limiting factor for exercise in the heat.

When exercising in the heat for the first time, many people experience some of the symptoms of heat illnesses, such as heat cramps, fainting and exhaustion. But the good news is that the occurrence and severity of these symptoms can be significantly reduced by a process of acclimatisation, which allows the body to adapt to the stresses of a warm environment gradually, by repeated exposure.

Complete heat acclimatisation requires up to 14 days of exposure, but adaptations occur at varying rates. Even as few as five days of heat exposure will allow some adaptation to increased environmental temperatures [2]. Within these five days, control of cardiovascular function improves, plasma volume increases, heart rate drops and blood flow is prioritised to reach active muscles and the skin surface. The increase in plasma volume is temporary, allowing the body to cope with the increased need for cooling by redirecting blood to the skin. Taken together, these short-term adaptations lower perception of work rate and allow toleration of the heat prior to longer-lasting changes.

These changes occur over the next week or so. Between days five and eight, the body's thermoregulatory response improves so that sweat rates increase and sweat production starts earlier, so boosting the dissipation of body heat by evaporative cooling. This process prevents body temperature rising critically and also allows for a reduction in skin blood flow as a means of cooling down core temperature, so increasing the blood available to supply active tissues.

Choose the right acclimatisation environment

By 10 days of heat exposure, sweat rates can be as much as doubled, although individual responses are as varied as individual sweat rates; (think of how some people are drenched in sweat after an hour's exercise while others are barely perspiring). Bear in mind, though, that hot dry climates produce different adaptations to sweat glands than hot humid ones, so you need to be sure that the environment you choose for acclimatisation closely matches that of your competition venue.

The early stages of heat acclimatisation see a drop in the loss of sodium chloride (salt) in sweat and urine, resulting in an increased extracellular fluid (ECF) volume. ECF includes the blood plasma, and this process helps the body to maintain a stable core temperature before the later thermoregulatory adaptations occur. ECF and plasma volume return to normal between days 8 and 14 [2].

Following heat acclimatisation, the body has improved efficiency and is better equipped to tolerate the demands of exercise. The heat-acclimatised athlete is able to exercise with a lower skin and core temperature and heart rate than an unacclimatised person. Since it is widely believed that reaching a critical core temperature limits exercise capacity, you can see how improving thermoregulatory mechanisms improves exercise tolerance. Additionally, muscle glycogen utilisation is reduced and post-exercise lactate concentration is lower [2].

Although excess fluid and salt intake will not enhance acclimatisation, dehydration or salt deficits will hamper the body's ability to respond to the heat stimulus, so it is important to maintain an adequate fluid intake during heat acclimatisation. Many studies have shown that dehydration markedly impairs exercise performance and recovery, so it follows that adequate hydration is crucial to a successful adaptation to heat.

Your ability to acclimatise is linked to your current level of fitness. A high VO₂max (>60ml.kg-1.min-1), for example, may enhance your ability to acclimatise and the speed at which you reach a stable acclimatised state. This may be because physiological adaptations to heat are similar to those experienced during hard training in a cool environment. Thus, for well-trained individuals, some of the adaptations – such as increased plasma volume, increased sensitivity of the sweat response and production of more dilute sweat – are already in place.

Passive heat exposure produces the same adaptations, and thus people who have lived in a warm climate all their lives have advantages denied to those from cooler climes.

If you are gradually acclimatising during a period of warm weather training, around 10 consecutive days of exercise are required, with 2-4 hours of heat exposure each day. The first two days should involve only light exercise lasting about 15-20 minutes, with a gradual build-up of duration and intensity.

For optimal acclimatisation, 24-hour exposure to the relevant environmental conditions is better than training in the heat, then resting in an air-conditioned room for the rest of the day. Some high-intensity exercise should be performed in the same heat and humidity as expected for the race, but only after

'People who have lived in a warm climate all their lives have advantages denied to those from cooler climes'

6Complete acclimatisation is not always possible for athletes because of the time requirement9

4-5 days of low-intensity exercise. This protocol combines both passive and active heat exposure to maximise adaptation without causing heat illness.

It is possible to assist the acclimatisation process by exercising in a heat chamber for 1-3 hours per day before departure, but this will be only partially effective and should be seen as an adjunct to, rather than a replacement for, full acclimatisation. Wearing impermeable clothing while exercising may also make a small contribution to the acclimatisation process.

Many laboratory studies examining the benefits of acclimatisation using heat chambers alone have reported improved cardiovascular adaptations. One such study, involving 100 minutes of treadmill walking in a heated chamber for nine consecutive days, showed a decrease in rectal temperature and heart rate and a rise in sweat loss over the study period [3].

Complete acclimatisation is not always possible for athletes because of the time requirement. And sometimes there is no time at all to acclimatise – such as on those occasions when temperatures suddenly soar. In such cases, you may need to take some short-term measures, such as pre-cooling, to prevent your performance being impaired by the heat.

Pre-cooling is a strategy that helps to prevent excessive overheating during exercise by reducing body temperature beforehand [4]. This introduces an increased margin for metabolic heat production, expanding the time during which you can exercise in comfort and safety. Pre-cooling has been shown in many studies to have a favourable effect on endurance exercise in hot environments [5]. It has been suggested that, as well as increasing time to fatigue, this process also enables athletes to pick up their pace towards the end of races and other events [6].

Pre-cooling can be achieved by means of either cold air exposure or cold water immersion. The former is not a practical option – unless you have access to a sports science lab or a large freezer! However, cold water immersion can be achieved simply by standing under a cold shower or filling a bath with water and ice. If taking the bath option, water should be gradually cooled, if possible, to avoid acute cold stress, with temperature starting at around 29°C and gradually reducing by no more than 2°C every 10 minutes for a total of about 60 minutes.

As well as being easier to organise than cold air exposure, cold water immersion also permits a greater rate of heat loss from the skin, a more uniform decrease in skin temperature and a greater reduction in core temperature [4]. *(For a more detailed consideration of pre-cooling, see the article on page 19).*

Fluid intake plays a vital role in the body's ability to tolerate heat, and is the most practical intervention strategy for coping with exercise in the heat. Acclimatisation will actually increase fluid needs because of increased sweat rates. By ensuring you replace these lost fluids, plasma volume can be maintained, allowing circulation and sweating to continue and making it easier for you to maintain exercise intensity and duration for longer.

Fluid replacement is top priority

Since carbohydrate conversion to energy is reduced during exercise in the heat, fluid ingestion is geared more to maintaining hydration than to replacing carbohydrate. A large volume of diluted fluid (around 2% carbohydrate) has been shown to be more beneficial in the heat, with increased time to exhaustion for endurance exercise, than no drink or a high-carbohydrate (15%) drink [7].

Even plain water is beneficial for maintaining plasma volume, but the addition of a small amount of salt will increase the volume of ingested water that remains in your body, which is especially important when sweat rates and electrolyte losses are high. A third of a teaspoon of table salt in a litre of water should be enough to improve water retention.

Given the large body of evidence relating dehydration to reduced performance during exercise in the heat, fluid replacement should be top of your list of priorities when preparing for warm weather competition. Prior hydration is also an important factor because if you are dehydrated before exercise begins, the reductions in your performance will be greatly magnified. Again, a dilute carbohydrate drink including a small amount of salt will suffice. *(For more on hydration see articles on pp55 & 69.)*

In conclusion, the successful competitor will have prepared for the heat with a strategy that includes acclimatisation, pre-cooling and hydration. The different elements involved in this process must be carefully planned and fitted to your schedule, with pre-cooling performed in the hours before the competition and hydration maintained throughout your training and race preparation. If practised and followed, these coping strategies should place you well ahead of the pack in terms of your ability to cope with the heat.

Clare Whitehead

References

1. *Medicine and Science in Sports and Exercise, vol 29, (9), p1240-1249, 1997*

2. *Encyclopaedia of Sports Medicine and Science, Internet Society for Sport Science, 1998.*

3. *Fed Proc, vol 22, p704, 1963*

4. *British Journal of Sports Medicine, vol 36, p89-94, 2002*

5. *Journal of Sports Sciences, vol 17, p937-944, 1999*

6. *Journal of Applied Physiology, vol 79, p1971-1976, 1996*

7. *Journal of Sports Sciences, vol 18, (5), p339-351, 2000*

Staying cool is still an issue in winter – and not just for endurance athletes

In cold weather, you're probably more concerned with staying warm than with devising strategies to cool your body even further. It is true that research has tended to focus on how body cooling can aid the performance of endurance athletes competing in hot, humid environments. But there is growing evidence that pre-cooling can offer performance advantages in a range of temperatures, during training as well as competition, and in non-continuous sports.

Exercise causes your body temperature to rise, and the harder you work the more rapid this rise will be. This rise in core temperature (Tc) can be modified by increased fitness but is exacerbated in hot and humid conditions. However, regardless of training state or climate, it is apparent that there is a critical limiting Tc at which athletes are forced to either reduce exercise intensity or risk heat-related illness.

Because the amount of heat stored in the body will limit the duration of exercise at a given intensity, it obviously makes sense to start exercising with as cool a body temperature as possible – *ie* by pre-cooling. In essence, the purpose of body cooling techniques is to increase the margin between your starting Tc and the Tc that will force you to reduce your pace.

Numerous studies have shown that pre cooling is advisable before prolonged exercise in hot temperatures, with evidence that it helps to sustain intensity and speed. In one study requiring subjects to run at 82% of max VO_2 in a heat chamber – 24°C and 51% relative humidity (RH) – pre-cooling by cold air exposure (5°C) was shown to boost performance by a massive 16% [1]. In another study, following a 20-minute cold water bath (23-24°C) the distance achieved during a 30-minute self-paced running test in hot humid conditions (32°C, 62%RH) increased by an average of 4% [2].

The effect of pre-cooling on self-paced performance was investigated further by Kay and his research group, who found that pre-cooling the skin alone (by 24°C water immersion) stretched 30 minutes of self-paced cycling in 31.4°C and 60.2%RH ambient conditions by 0.9k [3]. Kay suggested that, although there was no reduction in Tc, pre-cooling was effective in reducing thermal strain, thereby enabling the subjects to increase exercise intensity towards the end of the trial.

Other researchers have also suggested that the main benefit of pre-cooling is in enabling athletes to draw on reserves later in a performance due to reduced thermal strain, allowing for different pacing strategies and increased intensity in the later stages.

But what about those of us who don't get to compete in hot and humid conditions? Well, performance has also been shown to improve in lower ambient temperatures (Ta).

A group led by Olshewski employed a cold air method to cool their subjects and reported a whopping 12% improvement in a subsequent cycle test to exhaustion, performed in a Ta of 18°C [4]. Using a similar technique, another group of scientists reported significant work rate improvements and increases in absolute work performed during a cycle test performed in a Ta of 18°C [5]. Ambient temperatures of 18°C are commonplace for both indoor competition and typical northern European summer months. So from this evidence we can surmise that body cooling has a real role to play in improving performance on home turf.

Cooling between bouts

Few studies have focused on whether body cooling between bouts of exercise can also improve performance. Undoubtedly, increases in Tc create a problem in exercise of this nature, but the rest periods allow for some degree of cooling down. In the real world there is unlikely to be enough time to reduce Tc to resting levels, and the aim of any cooling strategy must be to gain a performance advantage by offsetting as much thermal strain as possible before the next bout.

A group of Texan scientists investigated the effects of body cooling during a 12-minute rest period between two bouts of exercise in a hot environment (38°C). They reported that pre-cooling (fan cooling with water spraying) resulted in a lower Tc and a reduced loss of body water throughout the second bout [6]. However, another study reported no significant physiological benefit from pre-cooling before the intermittent activity of a football game (2x45 minute periods, 15 minute intermission) [7].

6 I have used body cooling techniques with racket sport players to great effect 9

More studies are needed to investigate fully the potential benefits of body cooling for intermittent exercise performance, whether cooling is carried out pre-exercise or during a rest period. In my work as an applied sports scientist, I have used body cooling techniques with racket sport players to great effect; despite the relatively short rest periods between games, these sports lend themselves particularly well to cooling. The majority of evidence I have to support this claim is anecdotal, but if the athletes 'feel' and perform better, with no medical ill effects, I am more than happy to continue suggesting body cooling as an aid to performance in such sports.

Many of the 'take home messages' from the studies mentioned above can be transferred to the training arena, particularly if you are lucky enough to have access to indoor and/or warm-weather training facilities. Periods of reduced training volume as athletes acclimatise to warm weather training are expensive in terms of both money and time. And many of the athletes I work with employ cooling techniques before and during training sessions in such conditions, so allowing volume to be maintained despite a high ambient temperature.

It should be noted, however, that metabolic and cardiovascular responses can be affected during the initial 15 minutes of exercise after pre-cooling. These 'differences', including reduced heart rate and perceived exertion, are, in essence, the benefits of body cooling. During this period, it is advisable to use pacing as the best indication of intensity; otherwise there is a good chance that you will be working above your target zones.

A practical cooling method

By this point you may be beginning to think what a great idea body cooling is. But you've probably also noticed that cold air exposure or water immersion have been the predominant methods used, which may not be practicable in the real world. Exactly these thoughts occurred to scientists at the Australian Institute of Sport (AIS), who created a highly practical cooling jacket for their athletes, made from wet suit material and designed to be packed with ice.

Using these jackets, the AIS carried out maximal cycling trials in a heat chamber (32°C, 60%RH). Subjects wore the jackets for the first nine minutes of the protocol, leading to an average drop in skin temperature from 33.5°C to 12°C. On average, the subjects cycled for 1.1 minutes longer during the cooling trial than they were able to without the jackets and reported a lower perception of effort and thermal discomfort. Despite these differences in skin temperature and perceptions, however, the ice jacket did not affect Tc, heart rate or blood lactate [8].

Cooling jackets became commercially available following their use in the 1996 Olympic Games in Atlanta

In a further AIS heat chamber study reported to a conference I attended, the same jacket was worn during a 30-minute 'warm-up' prior to a maximal 2,000m rowing test, and the researchers found that average rowing times decreased by 2.8 seconds. These jackets became commercially available following their use in the 1996 Olympic Games in Atlanta.

The AIS has also demonstrated exercise improvement with an even simpler approach. Rowers completed a heat chamber (30°C, 30% RH) protocol involving a 10-minute warm-up and a six-minute all-out effort, separated by an eight-minute rest period. During the rest period, ice packed in damp towels was intermittently applied to the rowers' heads, faces, necks, arms and thighs – and the improved ergometer performance was equivalent to a four-second margin over a 2,000m race.

To summarise, the current body of evidence suggests that pre-cooling can increase performance capacity in various ambient temperatures and exercise circumstances. I should point out, as a note of caution, that over-cooling the body will not only hamper performance but also pose a health risk. However, it was never the aim of this article to advocate drastic techniques which can only be employed in a laboratory setting.

Here, in summary, are some pre-cooling tips derived from the scientific research:

- Ideally use a cooling jacket or, failing that, ice-packed damp towels;
- Make a reduction in skin temperature your major goal;
- Aim to pre-cool for 8-30 minutes during warm-ups and/or the intervals between warm-ups and competition;
- Be sure to practise your chosen pre-cooling technique before using it in a key event.

Andrew Harrison

References

1. *J Appl Physiol 1995; 79: 1971-6*

2. *Med Sci Sports Exerc 1997; 29: 943-9*

3. *J Sports Sci 1999; 17: 937-44*

4. *J Appl Physiol 1988; 68: 803-11*

5. *J Appl Physiol 1984; 57: 1731-7*

6. *J Strength & Cond Res 2001; 15(2): 247-254*

7. *Eur J Appl Physiol 2000; 81: 11-17*

8. *Med Sci Sports Exerc 1997; 29(5): S263*

Something in the air: the real problem facing the organisers of the recent Athens Olympics

One of the main preoccupations of national team leaders in the weeks leading up to the most recent Olympic Games in Athens was the environmental challenges that would confront their competitors. Everyone knew it was going to be hot but, as the Games drew closer, the full implications of holding them in one of Europe's most polluted cities became painfully clear [1].

Despite the sterling efforts of the Greek organising committee to reduce air pollution levels in time, many predicted that athletes would be affected by breathing problems on an unprecedented scale, while those with asthma would suffer potentially catastrophic exacerbation of their condition.

The Greek authorities strenuously denied these risks, claiming that competing in Athens was likely to be no more injurious to health than, say, in London. Maybe they were right – but what the debate highlighted was the growing concern over the impact of air pollution on the health of city-dwellers, especially those who exercise.

For those of who live and exercise in the city, the potential health risks of breathing a cocktail of air pollutants are a very real concern. Links between high levels of air pollution and lung disease [2], cardiovascular disease [3] and even cancer [4] are being established in the medical literature. For example, elevated levels of air pollution are closely associated with both an increased prevalence of asthma [5] and an increased incidence of acute exacerbation in all patients with cardio-respiratory illness [2,6].

A study presented at the American Heart Association's meeting in 2003 identified significant associations between cardiovascular disease deaths and a number of air pollutant concentrations [3], and it is estimated that pollution causes 19 premature deaths per 100,000 of population across Europe [1].

Although these mortality data refer to patients with pre-existing disease, they highlight the serious implications of exposure to air pollution. In addition, the accumulating evidence of an association between exposure to air pollution and the development of debilitating and potentially life-threatening illness should give all of us cause for concern.

Although it is now well established that breathing polluted air has a negative impact upon health, there is no direct evidence about the long-term health implications of exercising in a polluted environment. Common sense would suggest that if your lungs are exposed to 10 times the quantity of air during exercise than at rest, this must be equivalent to increasing exposure duration 10-fold; in other words, a one-hour exercise exposure is similar to a 10-hour resting exposure.

To add insult to injury, when you exercise you switch from nasal to oral breathing, which allows air to bypass your body's natural defence against inhaled particles – the elaborate filtering system that lies between your nose and the back of your throat.

To top it all, during exercise we inhale more deeply and rapidly than usual, which means that particles and other pollutants are carried to the deepest reaches of the lungs. Scary stuff!

So what air pollutants should we be concerned about, and how can city-dwellers find out about the daily risks of exercising outdoors?

Most TV and radio weather reports now provide information about air pollution (*eg* www.bbc.co.uk/weather), especially in the summer months when 'photochemical smog' becomes a problem. In addition, in the UK local information is available on Teletext, the internet (www.airquality.co.uk), or via freephone (0800 556677). Pollution levels are given a numerical indicator and banded to provide information about associated health risks, as follows:

⁶During exercise we inhale more deeply and rapidly than usual, which means that particles and other pollutants are carried to the deepest reaches of the lungs⁹

- **Low (1-3)** – effects unlikely to be noticed, even by those who are sensitive to air pollution;
- **Moderate (4-6)** – sensitive people may notice mild effects but these are unlikely to need action;
- **High (7-9)** – sensitive people may notice significant effects and may need to take action;
- **Very high (10)** – effects on sensitive people, described for high pollution, may worsen.

In the developed world, air pollutants come principally from vehicle exhaust emissions and are highest in urban areas; (with one exception – ozone is frequently highest in rural areas around cities, as it is a very mobile gas). The level of pollution on any given day and in any given city is determined by a combination of factors, not just the volume of vehicle traffic.

For example, cities like Athens have relatively high levels of air pollution because of local meteorology, topography and infrastructure. Athens is an industrialised, highly populated Mediterranean coastal city surrounded by mountains. In the summer, photochemical smog forms during the day in the strong sunlight and is confined by the surrounding mountains. At night, the direction of the sea breeze that had held the smog over the city reverses, and the smog cloud is drawn out to sea. However, the next day the sea breeze brings the smog back over the city, where its concentration is increased further by the daily dose of traffic fumes.

Other notorious smog hotspots are Bangkok, Beijing, London, Los Angeles, Mexico City, New Delhi, New York, Paris, Santiago de Chile, Sao Paulo, Sydney, and Vancouver. As we all know, the 2008 Olympics will be hosted by Beijing. Furthermore, London, Paris and New York are all front-runners to host the 2012 Games, so the issue of air pollution and Olympic competition venues looks set to run and run.

Not all vehicle emissions are harmful, but there are six that carry a health and/or performance impairment risk:
- carbon monoxide (CO)
- nitrogen dioxide (NO_2)

- ozone (O_3)
- particulate matter (PM10)
- sulphur dioxide (SO_2)
- volatile organic compounds (VOC).

Implications of chronic exposure

The full implications of chronic exposure to the cocktail of pollutants that city-dwellers breathe in every day are largely unknown, although some links have been made, as described above. Circumstantial evidence of a long-term health risk is strong for VOCs such as benzopyrene, which is a well-known carcinogen. VOCs contribute to the blue-brown haze associated with photochemical smog and also cause eye and respiratory tract irritation.

In terms of immediate detrimental influences to breathing and the oxygen transport system, high levels of carbon monoxide (CO) are associated with a decrease in the oxygen carrying capacity of the blood and a reduced maximal oxygen uptake and lactate threshold. Levels of CO are declining as more and more cars are fitted with catalytic converters, but there are peaks around congested roads, and concentrations are highest inside slow-moving cars, which has implications for athletes travelling to competitions by car.

The problem of PM10

Air pollution information also reports on air concentrations of particles less than 10 microns in size, so-called PM10. PM10 is a concern because it can be deposited in the deeper reaches of the lungs, and levels peak during smogs and at roadsides. The combination of PM10, sulphur dioxide and water vapour forms sulphuric acid-coated particles that deposit deep inside the lung, with fairly obvious consequences (irritation and asthma-like symptoms). The particles themselves are made up of a variety of compounds, including carcinogenic hydrocarbons and lead.

The deep, rapid breathing associated with exercise may enhance deposition of PM10 in the lungs, placing exercisers at increased risk. An increased risk of lung cancer has been demonstrated in Oslo residents whose homes were in the more polluted areas of the city[4], but the full implications of exposure to PM10 is currently unknown.

Nitrogen dioxide (NO_2) and sulphur dioxide (SO_2) are both very soluble gases that convert to nitric and sulphuric acid when they make contact with the moist lining of the mouth and lungs. They cause soreness of the nasopharynx and lungs, coughing and breathlessness, as well as inducing symptoms of asthma in both healthy people and asthmatics. Fortunately, concentrations of both gases are usually fairly low and these symptoms are very rare.

Unfortunately, the same cannot be said for ozone (O_3), which is good news in the stratosphere, where it filters out UV radiation, but very bad news at ground level (the troposphere). O_3 is formed by the action of strong sunlight on other atmospheric pollutants (principally VOC and NO_2), so concentrations are highest during summer. Because O_3 is very mobile, the highest concentrations are often found in the rural areas around cities. As with NO_2 and SO_2, O_3 induces asthma-like symptoms and lung inflammation. In addition to irritating the lungs directly, O_3 also acts on the nervous system to inhibit breathing, making it difficult and painful to take deep breaths; it has been suggested that this may be part of a protective reflex to minimise the lungs' exposure to the irritant.

Research has shown that responsiveness to O_3 is a function of concentration, exposure duration, and level of ventilation[7], which means its effects are magnified by exercise. There also appears to be large inter-individual variation in responsiveness to O_3, with some people showing large decrements in their lung function, while others show little or no ill effects[8,9].

The effects of exposure to ambient outdoor concentrations of O_3 were studied in a group of amateur cyclists during a summer competitive season in the eastern Netherlands[10]. The authors noted a significant relationship between ambient O_3 concentration and the cyclists' post-exercise lung function as well as wheeze, chest tightness and shortness of breath (worst

❛Ozone acts on the nervous system to inhibit breathing, making it difficult and painful to take deep breaths❜

when O_3 was highest). These relationships persisted when the observations at concentrations above 60 parts per billion (ppb) were excluded, suggesting that a detrimental influence remained, even on days when O_3 concentration would be deemed 'moderate'.

Ozone for asthmatics

Because of their pre-existing lung inflammation, asthmatics have been assumed to have a greater responsiveness to O_3 than people with normal lung function [11]. Interestingly, though, recent evidence suggests this may not be the case [12], and that asthma severity does not predict responsiveness [13]. However, there is evidence that lung inflammation in response to O_3 exposure may be more severe in asthmatics [14], which might have serious long-term implications, as well as leading to acute exacerbation of their condition [12].

It has also been demonstrated that O_3 exposure exacerbates responsiveness of asthmatics to other respiratory irritants, such as SO_2, which suggests it may be misleading to consider the detrimental effects of single pollutant challenges in laboratory studies [15].

Because O_3 triggers an inflammatory response within the lung, it has been suggested that supplementing the lungs' natural antioxidant capacity might increase their ability to withstand the oxidative stresses imposed by O_3 inhalation. In two studies from the same group in the Netherlands, competitive cyclists supplemented with antioxidant vitamins (approx 100mg vitamin E + 500mg vitamin C) had their lung function assessed before and after training or competition [16,17].

Supplementation was found to significantly reduce the O_3-induced decrements in lung function in both studies. These data are further supported by a study on street workers in Mexico City, who also demonstrated reduced lung function impairment when placed on a similar supplementation regimen [18].

So far, we've considered only the health-related implications of exposure to O_3, but there is also ample evidence that O_3 impairs exercise performance [19]. Recent unpublished research from Napier University in Scotland suggests that running time trial performance (8k) is impaired by around 1% while breathing an O_3 concentration of 100ppb, which is typical for a major city at the height of summer. The athletes in the study also suffered impaired lung function, coughing and breathing difficulties after the exercise bout. However, when antioxidant supplements were taken before a second time trial conducted with 100ppb O_3, performance was restored to the control level.

While a 1% decrement in time trial performance may not seem too bad, it would have a potentially disastrous impact on a world-class athlete competing in a major event. And, although levels of O_3 are typically low-to-moderate in the UK, during the summer heat wave of 2003, they reached record levels in major cities such as London (125ppb).

By now, you're probably wondering whether its just too risky to exercise at all in what we used to think of as the 'fresh air'. However, life is about managing risk; yes, you could damage your health by running along that dual carriageway, or cycling to work, but you could also be hit by a dozy driver. The solution is to be sensible about when and where you exercise and remember that air quality is poorest in urban areas, especially around heavily used and congested roads (although O_3 is the exception).

6Is it just too risky to exercise at all in what we used to think of as the fresh air?9

To minimise your risk without ruining your enjoyment of what remains a healthy activity, follow this advice:

- **Don't exercise…**
  …during rush hour;
  …in close proximity to a congested road;
  …in obvious smog;
  …when there is a combination of high vehicle emissions and strong sunlight.
- **Don't travel** to a competition in a poorly ventilated car through congested areas (CO concentrations are highest inside cars).

- **Do…**
  …check the pollution forecasts;
  …be particularly cautious if you have asthma. Use your inhaler before exercising and consult your GP if your

symptoms worsen, as you may need a change of medication;

…consider taking antioxidant vitamin supplements (100mg vitamin E + 500mg vitamin C);

…consider using a personal air filtration device (but be careful to check the manufacturer's claims against independent reports; not all masks perform as well as manufacturers would have you believe). Log onto http://news.bbc.co.uk/1/hi/health/latest_news/109656.stm.

Alison McConnell

References

1. www.apheisnet/pages/communications.htm

2. Monaldi Arch Chest Dis 57 (3-4), 156-60, 2002

3. www.americanheart. org

4. Thorax 58 (12), 1071-6, 2003

5. Respiration 71(1):51-9, 2004

6. Indian J Chest Dis Allied Sci 44 (1), 13-9, 2002

7. Am J Respir Crit Care Med 156 (3 Pt 1), 715-22, 1997

8. Arch Environ Health 46 (3), 145-149, 1991

9. Am J Respir Crit Care Med 151 (1), 33-40,1995

10. Am J Respir Crit Care Med 150 (4), 962-6, 1994

11. Environ Health Perspect 103 Suppl 2, 103-5, 1995

12. Mol Aspects Med 21 (1-2), 1-48, 2000

13. Eur Respir J 11 (3), 686-93, 1998

14. Res Rep Health Eff Inst 78, 1-37, discussion 81-99, 1997

15. Am Rev Respir Dis 141 (2), 377-80, 1990

16. Occup Environ Med 55 (1), 13-7, 1998

17. Am J Epidemiol 149 (4), 306-14, 1999

18. Am J Respir Crit Care Med 2002 Sep 1; 166 (5), 703-9

19. J Appl Physiol 61 (3), 960-6, 1986

ALTITUDE TRAINING

Reaching for new heights: is it all a waste of time and money?

The effects of training and, more recently, sleeping at high altitude on athletic performance have been studied in the West for more than 30 years. During that time, these practices have become an almost essential aspect of the preparation of world-class competitors. Yet the evidence base supporting a beneficial effect of altitude exposure for sea-level performance remains flimsy at best.

A telling analysis of the benefits of altitude exposure for sports performance was undertaken by François Peronnet and published in a letter to the editor of the *International Journal of Sports Medicine* in 1994 [1]. He analysed the mens' running speeds corresponding to the world record and 10 best performances per year over 1,500m, 5,000m and 10,000m from 1956 to 1991. Taking 1968 as the watershed marking the interface between the pre- and post-altitude training eras, he reasoned that if altitude training had made a positive contribution to performance, the rate of increase of running speeds should be steeper after this point.

The findings were striking. In 1968 the cream of the world's distance running talent trained at altitude in preparation for the Mexico City Olympics; despite this, no new world records were set in 1968 or the next four years. In fact, this was the longest period between 1956 and 1991 without a new world record; and furthermore, the rate of increase in world record and annual best performances was slower after 1968 than before. All in all the data suggest that, far from improving endurance performance, altitude training may even have exerted a detrimental effect.

Peronnet's analysis ceased in 1991, and the early 1990s marked another watershed in the altitude debate, which may place a different complexion on the outcome. But before exploring this it would be useful to examine the traditional rationale for high-altitude exposure. This rests primarily on the haematological (blood) adaptations that occur in humans exposed to a hypoxic (low oxygen) environment.

Ascent to high altitude is accompanied by a progressive fall in barometric pressure and an accompanying fall in the partial pressure of oxygen. The resulting decrease in arterial oxygen saturation (hypoxaemia) triggers a cascade of physiological disturbances that ultimately result in an increase in the production of red blood cells (RBCs), a process known as polycythaemia. The production of RBCs helps to improve the oxygen-carrying capacity of the blood, and hence maximal oxygen uptake (VO₂max).

One of the essential precursors to the increase in RBC formation is the release of erythropoietic factor (EPO) by the kidney, hence the (illegal) practice of injecting EPO to boost RBC production. While the benefits of this artificially-induced increase in RBC concentration are long established and well documented [2,3], the same is not true for altitude exposure, as I will explain. Early studies of the effects of altitude training focused on the RBC concentration changes and VO₂max as their physiological outcome parameters.

VO₂max and 'detraining' at altitude

As mentioned, high altitude is accompanied by a decrease in the partial pressure of oxygen which, in turn, leads to a reduction in the driving pressure for oxygen transport and a corresponding fall in VO₂max. The magnitude of this decline is around 5-7% per 1,000m [4]. An increase in altitude of as little as 600m has been shown to decrease the performance of cyclists in a five-minute cycle power test by 5.9% [5].

Thus, it is easy to see that one confounding influence on the outcome of altitude training is the progressive decline in VO₂max, which compromises training intensity, leading to 'detraining' at altitude. In the early 1990s, the 'live-high-train-low' (LHTL) model was developed to overcome this effect[6]. With LHTL, athletes sleep at simulated or real altitudes of around 2,500m but train at sea level. So what does the data from the past decade of LHTL tell us about the benefits of altitude exposure for sea-level performance?

The LHTL model was originally predicated on two assumptions:

1. That any benefit of altitude exposure was due to an increase in RBC concentration;
2. That sleeping at simulated altitude was enough to stimulate RBC production.

Studies from the originators of LHTL appear to support the notion that it boosts RBC production, VO₂max and running time trial performance. Levine and Stray-Gundersen went on to compare the effects of LHTL (2,500m and 1,250m), live-high-train-high (LHTH: 2,500m) and live-low-train-low (LLTL: 150m) over a four-week intervention[7].

The LHTL and LHTH groups both showed increases in VO₂max (5%) that were 'related' to the increase in their RBC volume (9%). However, only 14% of the variation in VO₂max could be explained by the change in RBC volume. Performance in a 5,000m running time trial improved only in the LHTL group, but again less than half (42%) of the variation in performance could be explained by the change in VO₂max.

6An increase in altitude of as little as 600m has been shown to decrease the performance of cyclists by 5.9%9

Altitude simulation with hypoxic tents

In this study, altitude exposure was achieved by physically travelling up a mountain. More recently, the LHTL methodology has been implemented with the aid of so-called altitude houses, or hypoxic sleeping tents. In both, the athlete sleeps at a simulated altitude of around 2,500m.

In their 2001 review, Hahn *et al* retrospectively analysed data from a series of six studies conducted in the Australian Institute of Sport altitude house in Canberra[8]. In four of the studies they examined the physiological adaptations stimulated by the

LHTL methodology. They observed an increase in serum EPO of 80% after the first 1-5 nights of exposure, but this declined to a level that was not significantly different from baseline or the control situation by the end of the intervention. Similarly, there was no significant increase in either reticulocyte formation (immature RBCs) or RBC mass, and VO_2max tended to decrease by comparison with baseline.

The only positive outcome across the four studies was that after a period of up to 23 days of LHTL there was a trend towards improved performance in exercise tasks lasting around four minutes. The researchers concluded that any benefits to performance of LHTL were unlikely to be due to an increase in RBC mass or VO_2max.

It is most likely that differences in the outcome of studies focusing on RBC mass and VO_2max are due to methodological factors. For example, Levine and Stray-Gundersen[7] noted an increase in RBC volume, but this was measured using a dye-injection technique that is now thought to overestimate RBC volume. In later research, using an isotopic labelling technique that is widely acknowledged to be the most reliable method of estimating RBC volume, a 13-day exposure to an altitude of 4,300m resulted in no change[9].

6It seems unlikely that performance improvements are due to changes in the oxygen transport system9

Where changes in VO_2max are concerned, an analysis of 17 studies examining the effect of hypoxia on sea-level VO_2max revealed a mean effect of +0.3% for hypoxia-exposed subjects, compared with -0.4% for control subjects[10]. The researchers concluded that there was very little evidence for an effect of hypoxic exposure on VO_2max and that differences between studies were probably due to biological variability and the random error of measurement.

Thus, if exposure to hypoxia does lead to performance improvements, it seems unlikely that these are due to improvements in the oxygen transport system. However, recent evidence is pointing to an unexpected benefit of LHTL. A number of studies have demonstrated a lower oxygen cost of steady-state cycling[11,12,13] and running[14,15] after exposure to hypoxia.

For example, in their study of 22 elite distance runners,

Saunders *et al* compared the influence of a 20-day programme of LHTL, live-moderate-train-moderate (LMTM: 1,500-2,000m) and LLTL (600m) [15]. The oxygen cost of running at three submaximal speeds was on average 3.3% lower after LHTL than after the other two interventions. There were no significant differences between or within groups for minute ventilation, heart rate, respiratory exchange ratio (R), or haemoglobin mass. Since there was also no difference in lactate concentration in the LHTL group, the lower oxygen cost of running could not be explained by an increase in anaerobic metabolism.

Similarly, the absence of a change in R failed to lend support to a proposed mechanism for improved mechanical efficiency following LHTL, *ie* increased utilisation of carbohydrate. The researchers were unable to offer any alternative explanation for their observations, but this was a carefully conducted study suggesting that improvement in mechanical efficiency in response to altitude exposure justifies further investigation. In high-performance athletes, variations in race performance are often attributable solely to differences in their mechanical efficiency, especially in running [16].

To date, only one study has examined the influence of LHTL on 'anaerobic' performance. Nummella and Rusko observed an improvement in 400m running performance (0.8%) after a 10-day LHTL intervention in eight athletes, by comparison with controls who undertook identical training but remained at sea level throughout [17]. The performance improvement was accompanied by increases in running speed at a range of lactate concentrations, as well as a reduction in perceived exertion.

The researchers speculated that the improved 400m performance might have been due to an increase in muscle-buffering capacity. This suggestion is supported by the observations of Gore *et al*, who observed an increase in the muscle-buffering capacity of six cyclists/triathletes after a 23-night LHTL intervention [11]. However, in another study that same group detected no change in muscle-buffering capacity in 29 cyclists/triathletes following a 20-night programme of LHTL [18]. The researchers suggested that the discrepancy might be due to the slightly higher simulated altitude used in their first study (3,000 v 2,650m).

Interestingly, the second study did identify a significant lowering of blood lactate concentration during exercise at 85% VO_2max. However, this could not be ascribed to a change in the abundance of lactate transport proteins (monocarboxylate transporters MCT1 and MCT4), which remained unchanged. The researchers suggested that these transporters were already up-regulated by the subjects' ordinary training and, further, that the overall pattern of response of the lactate system was consistent with a muscle cellular adaptation that reduced the rate of lactate production and facilitated oxidative energy provision.

Intermittent hypoxic training
Thus, there is some preliminary evidence that LHTL may also be beneficial for athletes whose competitive events rely heavily upon anaerobic metabolism.

An alternative method of utilising hypoxia to improve exercise performance is to train high and live low (THLL), also known as intermittent hypoxic training (IHT). This methodology has a long history in the former Soviet Union, going back as far as the 1930s [19]. The Soviets were interested in the effects of acute exposure to hypoxic environments on early aviators who flew in open cockpits. In its modern guise, IHT is based upon the rationale that exercising in hypoxia enhances muscle adaptations to training.

In a meticulous review of the research output of scientists working in the former Soviet Union, Serebrovskaya recently provided access to a wealth of data that was not previously accessible to western scientists [19]. Of particular interest in the context of athletic performance was data on local muscle adaptations in response to IHT. For example, Serebrovskaya suggests that the Soviet data provides evidence of a range of mitochondrial adaptations that increase the efficiency of oxygen utilisation in the production of ATP (adenosine triphosphate – the body's universal energy donor).

The western literature examining the effects of training in

moderate hypoxia (IHT) is far less abundant than that examining the LHTL methodology. An early study used an elegant unilateral exercise model, in which 10 subjects exercised one leg while breathing room air and the other while breathing a gas mixture containing 13.5% oxygen (about 3,250m) for 30 minutes at a time, three days per week over an eight-week period[20].

They observed an increase in single leg VO₂max and oxidative enzyme activities in both legs, but there was a greater increase in the activity of the mitochondrial aerobic enzyme citrate synthase in the hypoxically trained leg. There were also trends for increased activity of succinate dehydrogenase (another aerobic enzyme) and phosphofructokinase (an important regulator enzyme for glycolysis) in the hypoxically trained leg. Increased activity of these enzymes is normally associated with improved aerobic and anaerobic capacity following training. The greater improvements in the hypoxically-trained leg suggest that the normal training response may be enhanced by hypoxia.

❛The normal training response may be enhanced by hypoxia❜

Contradictions in the literature

The finding of an increase in oxidative enzyme activity is unique to training in hypoxia, since LHTL has not been shown to induce such changes. However, a subsequent study failed to replicate the finding of a greater effect of training in hypoxia on citrate synthase activity, although this may have been due in part to the use of a lower simulated altitude (2,500m)[21].

Changes in anaerobic performance were noted in a later study involving eight triathletes who trained under hypoxic conditions (2,500m) for two hours per day for 10 days, and a matched control group undertaking the same training at sea level[22]. The hypoxically-trained athletes showed improvements in performance during a Wingate Anaerobic test (mean power, peak power and time to peak power and VO₂max) that were not observed in the control group. In slight contrast, a study on non-endurance-trained subjects observed greater improvements in VO₂max in hypoxically-trained subjects, but only when measured under hypoxic conditions[23].

Once again, the picture for IHT is clouded by contradictions within the literature. For example, the most enthusiastic proponents of LHTL [7,24] have also published a study showing no additional benefit of IHT above normoxic training [25]. This study compared the effects of IHT and normoxic training on high intensity performance in 16 swimmers and noted no differences in time trial performance over 100m or 400m between the two groups.

The discrepancy between the results of this study and those reported in the previous paragraph is probably due to differences in the magnitude and duration of the IHT stimulus and outcome measures between studies. In the swimming study, subjects trained for only eight weeks, at a lower simulated altitude (2,500m) and with less frequent (three times per week) and much shorter bouts of hypoxic exposure (around 12.5 min of high-intensity exercise and 10 min of rest between repetitions and sets). Previous studies with positive outcomes from IHT have typically trained subjects in hypoxia for periods of at least 30 minutes, five days per week [22, 23].

6 The jury is still out on the role of hypoxia as an ergogenic aid 9

To date, the theoretical rationale favouring IHT is probably stronger than the evidence from studies directly assessing its influence on physical performance. There appears to be some evidence of adaptations at muscle level, including increases in the activities of oxidative enzymes, mitochondrial volume and capillary length. This is supported by evidence of an increase in the gene expression of a range of factors with the potential to influence muscle metabolism and, possibly, performance [26].

This latter study compared the effects of training in hypoxia (3,850m) and normoxia at two training intensities for 30 minutes at a time, five days per week over a period of six weeks. The most potent stimulus was high intensity hypoxic training, which resulted in sub-cellular changes that could theoretically improve the muscles' performance. In fact, though, there was no evidence of any functional benefit from these changes, since neither VO_2max nor peak power output during the incremental test differed significantly between the groups.

So there you have it. The literature tends to support the idea that the live-high-train-low model has beneficial effects on mechanical efficiency, but probably not (as has been assumed for many years) on systemic oxygen transport. By contrast, intermittent hypoxic training appears to elicit muscle biochemical and structural adaptations that may, under some conditions, result in improvements in VO_2max and anaerobic performance. Since both LHTL and IHT appear to exert their influence on performance via the muscles, it seems sensible that future studies should focus on muscular mechanisms. At this time, however, the jury is still out on the role of hypoxia as an ergogenic aid.

What does this mean for athletes and coaches? In practical terms, those considering altitude training should be cautious about investing a large amount of time and money in a practice that will, at best, yield only minor benefits and at worst may even be detrimental to sea-level performance.

If you are really committed to giving it a try, the cheapest and safest option would be to use a sleeping tent.

If, however, you are obliged to compete at high altitude, some acclimatisation will be essential. In this case, a 4-6-week block of inspiratory muscle training before your acclimatisation trip will help to overcome the huge increase in respiratory effort sensation that occurs in everyone attempting to train above 1,500.

Alison McConnell

References

1. *Int J Sports Med 15(6):335-6, 1994*

2. *Med Sci Sport Exerc 16:256-262, 1984*

3. *Haematologica 85:564-572, 2000*

4. *Aviat Space Environ Med 69:793-801, 1998*

5. *Eur J Appl Physiol 75:136-143, 1997*

6. *Med Sci Sport Exerc 23:S25, 1991*

7. *J Appl Physiol 83:102-112, 1997*

8. *Comp Biochem Physiol 128:777-789, 2001*

9. *Sports Medicine 31:533-557, 2001*

10. *J Appl Physiol 81:636-642, 1996*

11. *Acta Physiol Scand 173:275-286, 2001*

12. *J Appl Physiol 89:1189-1197, 2000*

13. *Can J Appl Physiol 26: 143-156, 2001*

14. *High Alt Med Biol 4:291-304, 2003*

15. *J Appl Physiol 96: 931-937, 2004*

16. *Med Sci Sports Exerc 32(6):1130-4, 2000*

17. *J Sport Sci 18:411-419, 2000*

18. *J Appl Physiol 96: 517-525, 2004*

19. *High Alt Med Biol 2:205-221, 2002*

20. *Med Sci Sports Exerc 29:238-243, 1997*

21. *Eur J Appl Physiol 85:486-490, 2001*

22. *Eur J Appl Physiol 84:283-290, 2001*

23. *Int J Sports Med 22:579-585, 2001*

24. *J Appl Physiol 91:1113-1120, 2001*

25. *J Appl Physiol 94:733-743, 2003*

26. *J Appl Physiol 91:173-182, 2001*

COLD WEATHER EXERCISE

How to protect your performance as well as your health against the chill winds of winter

Exercising and competing in cold weather conditions poses fewer risks to health and performance than working in extreme heat. However, there are a number of environmental threats to guard against and a variety of ways to safeguard your performance as well as your health in the less-than-perfect conditions.

The human temperature is tightly controlled to within about 1°C either side of 37°C (core temperature) or 33°C (skin temperature), although it is possible to survive a fall in core temperature of around 10°C and an increase of about 6°C[1]. The balance between heat gained and heat lost is tightly regulated to maintain thermal homeostasis, or balance.

During exercise, the two most powerful challenges to this thermal balance are metabolic heat production and environmental conditions.

Metabolic heat production is most likely to vary as a result of muscular activity, including exercise and shivering. In fact, humans are only 25% efficient, with 75% of the chemical energy produced during muscular contraction being lost as heat. This is necessary because during sustained vigorous exercise heat production can exceed 20 calories per minute. If the body were prevented from losing any of the heat it produced, a fatal level of heat storage would be reached in about four hours at rest and after just 25 minutes of moderate exercise!

The primary aim of the body's thermoregulatory system is to

maintain body temperature within safe limits. This is achieved by a complex combination of mechanisms.

In air at 25-28°C, or water at 35°C, a naked, resting individual can maintain body temperature by varying the amount of heat delivered to the skin via the circulation. As air/water temperature falls or increases, the body attempts to defend its temperature via shivering or sweating. However, these responses are limited in their effectiveness and costly in metabolic terms.

Cold environmental conditions pose a significant challenge to the maintenance of core temperature. If this falls low enough to affect physiological function, hypothermia may develop, leading to a variety of complications *(see table opposite)*. And if skin temperature falls dramatically, cold injury, including frostbite, may occur.

These risks are particularly high for older people, whose ability to maintain core temperature is reduced, and those with circulatory problems. Children also have a reduced ability to maintain core temperature because of their high body surface area:body mass ratio. They are able to safeguard their core temperature, in part, by constricting the peripheral blood vessels, but this increases their risk of suffering cold injury, such as frostbite.

The impact of cold on an athlete varies according to whether he or she is exercising in air or water. Water is 25 times more conductive than air, and heat is lost 3-5 times faster than with air at the same temperature [2].

Obviously, the temperature of air or water has a marked effect on the rate of heat loss, as do factors like wind speed, body composition and body size. People with a high body surface area:body mass ratio – *ie* tall slender people – lose heat at a faster rate than their short, heavy counterparts. That is because body fat is the key insulator, and those with plenty of it lose heat at the slowest rate.

It is also important to note that on dry land a wet person will lose heat at a faster rate than a dry one. This means that cold weather poses greater-than-normal risks if it is snowing or

6Water is 25 times more conductive than air, and heat is lost 3-5 times faster than with air at the same temperature9

Risk factors for hypothermia[1]

Hypothermia exists when deep body temperature falls below 35°C. Risk factors include:

- Cold air/water temperature;
- Air/water movement: faster moving fluids increase convective heat loss;
- Age: children cool faster than adults due to their lower levels of subcutaneous fat and higher surface area:mass ratio;
- Body stature: tall thin individuals cool faster than short fat people;
- Body morphology: body fat and unperfused muscle are good insulators;
- Gender: females tend to have more subcutaneous fat than men;
- Fitness: high fitness enables higher heat production;
- Fatigue: exhaustion results in decreased heat production;
- Nutritional state: hypoglycaemia (low blood sugar) reduces shivering and accentuates cooling;
- Intoxication: drugs and alcohol have depressant effects on metabolism;
- Lack of appropriate clothing.

raining, or if an individual is sweating excessively due to inappropriate clothing.

The skin is the first tissue to cool on exposure to low environmental temperatures; next affected are the superficial nerves and muscles, with knock-on effects on function.

Below a muscle temperature of 27°C, the contractile force and rate of force application is reduced and fatigue occurs earlier. Maximum power output falls by 3% per °C fall in muscle temperature [3]. And, in consequence, speed of movement, dexterity, strength and mechanical efficiency are all reduced with cooling.

During low-intensity exercise in air, including walking, there is a danger that heat production will not be sufficient to counteract heat loss unless precautions are taken. In this context, appropriate clothing is of key importance, although it is important to strike a balance between the need to maintain core/skin temperature and the need to avoid excessive insulation.

Over-insulation leads to a rise in core temperature and sweat production and, consequently, to wet clothing that may affect heat balance, particularly if exercise intensity falls.

Of greater concern, though, is the potential for cold injury to the extremities – hands, face and feet. In cold air or water, skin cooling is initiated in order to reduce heat loss. The extremities are most vulnerable to this skin cooling because of their high surface area:mass ratio, and the fact that their major source of heat – blood flow – is restricted to protect the vital organs.

During moderate and high intensity exercise in air, such as running or cycling, while performance may be reduced at temperatures below –10°C there is little concern for core temperature, although obviously care must be taken to avoid cold injury to the extremities. Similar findings have been observed for maximal and supramaximal exercise in the cold.

In cold water, a fall in core body temperature intensifies shivering, which raises oxygen consumption during submaximal exercise (by 9% in water at 25°C and 25.3% at 18°C). Thus, the energy cost of submaximal exercise is increased in water cooler than 26°C, and this can lead to more rapid depletion of carbohydrate and fat supplies, with earlier onset of fatigue.

VO_2max and maximum performance are both reduced during cold water immersion. This reduction occurs in water temperature as high as 25°C and is linked to falls in core body temperature, with a 10-30% reduction for every 0.5-2°C fall in core temperature. At the same time, lactate appears in the blood at lower workloads and accumulates more rapidly, suggesting a decreased oxygen supply to the muscle and greater reliance on anaerobic metabolism.

A decrease in core body temperature of 0.5°-1.5°C leads to a reduction of 10-40% in the capacity to supply oxygen to meet the increased requirements of activity. With more profound cooling, anaerobic metabolism is also reduced due to muscle cooling and direct impairment of the processes that produce anaerobic energy.

Regardless of exercise intensity, athletes must be careful to avoid rapid cooling after exercise, when exercise-induced heat production is reduced and heat is lost to the environment. The body responds in two ways to this negative thermal balance:

1. The peripheral blood vessels constrict, reducing blood flow to the skin and increasing central blood volume and central venous pressure. The reduction in blood flow varies across different body parts, leaving some areas of skin more susceptible to cold injury than others. In response to the increased venous pressure, blood pressure increases and, despite a cold-induced reduction in heart rate, cardiac output rises;

2. Involuntary metabolic heat production occurs, leading first to increased skeletal muscle tone (pre-shivering) and eventually to outright shivering.

⁶The rate of dehydration in the cold can be as high or even greater than you would expect in warm conditions⁹

Avoiding cold injury

Individuals vary in their response to cold exposure, with some more affected than others. But it is important for everyone to reduce heat loss following exercise in cold environments in order to avoid possible cold injury. The key protective measures are to get out of the cold environment as quickly as possible, remove wet clothing and add extra layers, taking care to cover high risk areas such as hands, feet and head.

It is worth pointing out that energy consumption, particularly of carbohydrates, increases when exercising in the cold, so it is a good idea to ingest more carbohydrate than usual under these conditions. Note, too, that the rate of dehydration in the cold can be as high or even greater than you would expect in warm conditions, for the following reasons:

- Inappropriate clothing can lead to an excessive rise in core temperature, giving rise to high sweat rates (a problem affecting not just hydration status but also post-exercise cooling rates);
- Increased blood pressure associated with constriction of the peripheral blood vessels can boost urine production;
- Because cold air tends to be dry, large volumes of fluid are lost through respiration.

These three factors combine to cause significant dehydration during prolonged exercise in the cold. It is therefore important to increase fluid intake in the cold to as much as, or more than, in warm conditions.

'Thawing out a freezing cold injury can be intensely painful, and strong painkillers should be given as necessary'

Pronounced constriction of the peripheral blood vessels during cold exposure can reduce skin temperature in the extremities to levels that may lead to cold injuries. Early warning signs of cold injury include tingling, numbness and/or a burning sensation in the fingers, toes, ears or nose. If protective action is not taken at this point, tissue damage may occur, giving rise to either 'freezing' cold injury (FCI, or frostbite) or non-freezing cold injury (NFCI).

Human tissue freezes at around –0.55°C. Nevertheless, the risk of frostbite is low above air temperatures of –7°C, irrespective of wind speed. It becomes pronounced when ambient temperature is below –25°C, even at low wind speeds.

NFCI is caused by protracted exposure to low ambient temperatures in the absence of freezing. Immobility, posture, dehydration, low fitness, inadequate nutrition, constricting footwear, fatigue, stress or anxiety, concurrent illness or injury can all raise the risk of NFCI. Its precise cause is poorly understood but appears to be related to damage to the walls of peripheral blood vessels.

Treatment depends on whether the dominant injury is FCI or NFCI. All cases of FCI should be thoroughly re-warmed by immersion of all the chilled parts in stirred water at 38-42°C. A topical anti-bacterial should also be diluted into the water bath. Re-warming should be delayed, however, if there is a chance that refreezing may occur.

Thawing out a freezing cold injury can be intensely painful, and strong painkillers should be given, as necessary. The best continuing treatment is twice-daily 30-minute immersion of the affected part in a 38-42°C whirlpool bath containing an appropriate anti-bacterial.

By contrast, people with NFCI should have their affected extremities re-warmed slowly, by exposure to warm air alone, and must not have them immersed in warm water. The early period after re-warming can be very painful in NFCI, even in the absence of obvious tissue damage. With either form of injury, once re-warmed, the affected extremities should be treated by exposure to air and early mobilisation.

It is unusual for the respiratory tract and lungs to be in danger of damage when exercising in the cold. The air is warmed and moistened rapidly during inspiration to avoid potential damage. However, this moistening/humidification of the inspired air can dry out the airways, giving rise to such complaints as dry mouth, a burning sensation in the throat and general irritation of the respiratory tract.

Cold air inhalation may aggravate symptoms of pre-existing asthma and even cause exercise-induced asthma in otherwise healthy athletes. The risk of all these problems can be reduced by wearing a scarf or face mask that will enhance air humidification and reduce water loss.

Rarely is it too cold to exercise if the correct precautions are taken. In general, however, when the temperature falls to below −20°C extreme caution should be taken, and exercise avoided.

Greg Whyte

References

1. Tipton, M (2004) Environmental factors. In ABC of Sports and Exercise Medicine ed Whyte, G, Harries, M and Williams, C, BMJ Books, London

2. Nimmo, M (2004) Exercise in the cold. Journal of Sports Sciences (in press)

3. Reilly, T and Waterhouse, J (2004) Exercise in the cold. pp33-49. In Sport, Exercise and Environmental Physiology, Elsevier Ltd, London

Sports drinks or water: what is the best choice for sports performers?

What does the term sports nutrition conjure up in your mind? Carbohydrate and protein? Vitamins and minerals? Or maybe the more exotic ergogenic aids like creatine? Whatever springs to mind, I bet it isn't water. Yet water is of supreme, overriding importance to both your health and performance.

Your body might appear solid, but it's actually much more like a bag of salty water, containing a few bones to maintain its shape. Water accounts for around 70% of your body weight – that's eight stone of water in an 11-stone adult! However, the loss of even a tiny fraction of this water can significantly reduce your performance, which is why maintaining good hydration is vital for all serious athletes.

Water is the medium in which the biochemistry of the body takes place. Every one of our trillions of cells both contains and is bathed in a watery medium. It's hardly surprising, therefore, that we have developed mechanisms for keeping the water content of the body pretty constant. Because some water is continually being lost in urine (in the process of excreting waste products), a constant throughput of water is required to maintain fluid balance. This balance is controlled principally by the kidneys and the thirst mechanism. When total body water drops, hormonal messages are sent to the brain to create thirst. Excessive water intake, on the other hand, stimulates an increase in urine production.

As well as providing the perfect chemical environment for our bodies, water has another extraordinary property – the ability to stop our bodies overheating by evaporating via the skin in the form of sweat. This is particularly important during exercise, when heat output rises dramatically.

At rest, the average 70kg adult consumes around 0.25 litres of oxygen per minute, which equates to about 70 watts of heat output. But when running at six-minute-mile pace, oxygen consumption rises 16-fold to over four litres per minute and heat output rises to over 1,100 watts! Unless the ambient temperature is sufficiently low, this extra heat cannot be radiated or carried away through convection quickly enough to prevent heat build up, so heat loss via evaporative cooling (*ie* sweating) has to occur.

For a 70kg runner running at this pace, the approximate energy burn rate is around 1000kcal per hour. In warm conditions it would take over 1.5 litres per hour of sweat evaporation to remove the extra heat generated. When you take into account the fact that some sweat will drip off the skin

---

Hyponatraemia – the dangers of fluid overload

Hyponatraemia is a disorder in fluid-electrolyte balance that results in an abnormally low plasma sodium concentration (less than 135mmol per litre compared with a normal range of 138-142mmol/L). A sustained decrease in plasma sodium concentration disrupts the dynamics of water exchange (osmotic balance) across the blood-brain barrier, resulting in a rapid influx of water into the brain. This can cause swelling in the brain, leading to a series of increasingly severe neurological responses, such as confusion, seizure, coma – even death.

The lower the blood sodium and the faster it falls, the greater the risk of life-threatening consequences. A drop in plasma sodium concentration to 125-135 mmol/L often results in little more than gastrointestinal symptoms, such as bloating and nausea. Below 125 mmol/L, the symptoms become more severe and can include confusion, throbbing headache, wheezy breathing, swollen hands and feet, unusual fatigue and reduced co-ordination. Below 120 mmol/L, the risk of seizure, coma and death is increased.

Hyponatremia in athletes is often, although not always, caused by excessive drinking. During exercise, urine production is decreased, reducing the body's ability to excrete excess water, while at the same time sodium losses are increased through sweating. The combined effect makes it much more likely that the body's sodium content will be significantly diluted.

without contributing to evaporative cooling, it is easy to see how runners can lose two litres of fluid per hour or more in hot conditions. And since fluid losses of just 2% of body weight (that's 1.5 litres from our 70kg runner) can cause a significant drop in performance, our mythical runner could be in trouble in less than an hour without taking extra fluid on board!

Because even small losses of water can cause a drop in performance, optimum hydration is extremely important to athletes. However, replacing fluid lost in sweat and urine is not the only justification for boosting fluid intake. Glycogen (stored muscle carbohydrate) is the body's principle fuel for high intensity activities, and replenishing glycogen stores with dietary carbohydrate is vital to continuing high performance.

‹Replacing fluid lost in sweat and urine is not the only justification for boosting fluid intake›

But the process of 'fixing' carbohydrate into muscles in the form of glycogen also requires water; each gram of glycogen fixed into muscle fibres requires around 3g of water, which is why you often feel thirsty after a high-carbohydrate post-training meal. If you don't drink to aid this process, water is simply drawn out of the bloodstream, leading to dehydration.

Fluid, then, is vital for adequate recovery – not just to replace water lost through sweating, but also to help replenish lost glycogen.

A comprehensive hydration strategy involves ensuring good hydration before training/competition, maintaining it during exercise and then replacing any shortfall as soon as possible afterwards. However, hydration isn't just about water: fluid loss via urine and, especially, sweating involves the loss of electrolyte minerals – calcium, magnesium, sodium, potassium and chloride. Although the composition varies from person to person (partly as a function of acclimatisation) a litre of sweat typically contains the following [1,2]:

- Calcium – 0.02g
- Magnesium – 0.05g
- Sodium – 1.15g
- Potassium – 0.23g
- Chloride – 1.48g

'Drinking pure water effectively dilutes the concentration of electrolyte minerals in the blood, which can impair a number of normal physiological processes'

There are three reasons why replacing these minerals by means of an electrolyte mineral-containing drink may be better then drinking pure water alone:

1. Although the amounts lost in sweat are generally small in proportion to total body stores, prolonged heavy sweating can lead to significant mineral losses (particularly of sodium). Drinking pure water effectively dilutes the concentration of electrolyte minerals in the blood, which can impair a number of normal physiological processes. An extreme example of such an impairment is 'hyponatraemia', when low plasma sodium levels can be literally life threatening *(see box on p56)*.

2. Drinks containing electrolyte minerals – particularly sodium – are known to promote thirst, thereby stimulating a greater voluntary intake of fluid [3]. There is also evidence that drinks containing sodium enhance the rate and completeness of re-hydration after a bout of exercise [4].

3. When the electrolyte minerals – again particularly sodium – are present in appropriate concentrations, the rate of fluid absorption from the small intestine into the rest of the body appears to be enhanced, especially in conjunction with small amounts of glucose [5]. This is particularly **important** when rapid uptake of fluid is required, such as during strenuous exercise in the heat.

Some athletes use glycerol to induce a state of hyper-hydration before long events in very hot conditions *(see box opposite for the pros and cons of this approach)*. However, if the fundamental dietary and normal fluid intake patterns are right, good pre-training/competition hydration will be the norm – not something that requires special attention a few hours before the event!

As for post-training/competition rehydration, the most reliable indicator is body weight, and your fluid replacement needs are considered in detail in the next article *(page 67)* of this issue. Research evidence suggests that fluids containing significant amounts of electrolytes (especially sodium) have a slightly greater impact in restoring hydration than fluids with little or no electrolytes/sodium [6].

Gycerol myths and reality

For most people, taking a glycerol/water solution before an event produces an increase in total body water (hyper-hydration). The question, however, is whether this extra water in the body actually enhances performance, and to date there is no clear-cut evidence to suggest that it does. It is true that after ingestion glycerol stays in the body and holds water with it, but the unanswered question is whether this extra water increases hydration within the cells or simply increases the amount of water swilling around in general circulation?

Overall, the current weight of evidence is tilted slightly in favour of a glycerol hyper-hydration protocol, but only in events where substantial dehydration is likely to be a problem. Moreover, there is still no agreement about the best way to take glycerol solution, or about whether certain kinds of plain water hyper-hydration protocols might offer similar benefits.

Unless your event is long and taking place in hot/humid conditions, resulting in unavoidable dehydration, there is probably little point in using glycerol. Not only are there unlikely to be any performance benefits, but glycerol ingestion can cause stomach upsets, together with headaches and blurred vision at higher doses. If you are tempted to try glycerol, make sure you've tried other hydration methods first. Glycerol should be considered only as a last resort.

However, the amount of sodium in the drink is critical. American scientists compared rehydration efficiency using each of the following [7]:

- a 6% carbohydrate solution with no added sodium;
- a 6% carbohydrate solution with 25mEq (0.58g) of sodium per litre;
- a 6% carbohydrate solution with 50mEq (1.16g) of sodium/L.

The subjects dehydrated by 3% of body weight during 90 minutes of exercise and drank as much as they wanted of one of the above beverages during a three-hour recovery period. The researchers found that the beverage with 25mEq of sodium per litre stimulated the greatest fluid intake, while the high sodium drink either suppressed thirst or diminished the palatability of the fluid.

Although many athletes fail to get it right, maintaining optimum hydration before and after exercise is a relatively straightforward process. Staying hydrated on the move, however, is a different story. When fluid losses are rapid (*ie* in hot, humid conditions), large amounts of fluids need to be absorbed quickly to maintain hydration status. But hydrating an exercising human body is not as simple as topping up a leaking bucket! The rate of fluid absorption in the body is determined by a two-stage process:

- Gastric emptying – how quickly ingested fluid leaves the stomach. In more dilute solutions, this is often the key step that determines the overall rate of fluid absorption;
- Intestinal absorption – the rate of absorption across the intestinal wall.

Optimal fluid absorption requires rapid gastric emptying and efficient uptake in the intestine.

Contrary to what you might expect, fluid absorption tends to take place in the small intestine rather than the stomach. Studies have shown that the larger the volume of fluid in the stomach, the more rapid the emptying into the small intestine, which means that maintaining a large fluid volume in the stomach by repeated drinking will maximise the rate of fluid (and nutrient) delivery to the small intestine [8,9].

Gastric emptying rate is also influenced by fluid composition. Early studies showed that, regardless of their electrolyte or glucose content, solutions with a lower overall concentration (or osmolality) than body fluids were emptied as rapidly as plain water [10,11]. With glucose solutions, for example, this would allow for a concentration of up to 2.5% (2.5g per litre of water). At the time it seemed that concentrations above this threshold would slow gastric emptying. But more recent work has established that drinks containing glucose concentrations of up to around 4-5% are emptied as rapidly as water [12].

Beyond a concentration of 5%, glucose solutions are emptied more slowly from the stomach, but they can nevertheless result in a faster delivery of glucose overall [13]. This is because the increase in glucose per unit volume delivered by these more concentrated drinks more than makes up for the reduced volume absorbed; where fluid replacement is of a lesser importance than energy replacement, more concentrated drinks may be preferable.

In recent years, there has been a growing trend towards the use of short chain glucose polymers, such as maltodextrins, in fluid/energy replacement drinks. The theory is that glucose polymers are emptied more rapidly from the stomach than pure glucose.

However, the evidence is far from conclusive and the various studies that have been carried out have reached conflicting conclusions [14-17]. This may be because concentrated beverages are known to increase the volume of gastric and intestinal secretions. It's possible, therefore, that the total volume of stomach contents may have been greater when solutions containing glucose rather than polymers were drunk, even though the amount of the ingested drink remaining in the stomach was the same. This would affect gastric emptying rates (remembering that gastric emptying is more rapid with high volumes of fluid in the stomach).

However, while the evidence that glucose polymers can offer a significant advantage over pure glucose is thin on the ground, there's almost no evidence to suggest that the emptying rate of polymer solutions is slower than that of free glucose solutions with the same energy content. Indeed, most studies have reported that polymer solutions are generally emptied faster, if not significantly so.

After gastric emptying, ingested fluids are absorbed in the small intestine. Pure water, or very dilute solutions, diffuse readily across the intestine. However, research has shown that dilute glucose/electrolyte solutions with a concentration that is slightly less than that of plasma maximise the rate of water absorption [18]. The researchers found that optimum hydration from the intestine was obtained with a solution containing 60mEq (1.38g) of sodium and 111mmols (20.0g) glucose per litre of water.

Where energy (*ie* glucose) replacement is the main goal, studies have shown that uptake from the small intestine into the

6Hydrating an exercising human body is not as simple as topping up a leaking bucket!9

body rises as the concentration of glucose rises in the intestine. This is simply because there is more glucose available per unit volume for absorption.

However, very concentrated solutions of glucose (more than 6%) can have an adverse effect on fluid balance. This is due to the process known as osmosis, whereby water separated by a permeable membrane (in this case the intestinal wall) passes from a more dilute to a more concentrated solution. When you ingest a drink with a very high concentration of glucose, the fluid in the bloodstream (on the other side of the intestinal wall) will be relatively dilute by comparison. And the osmotic pressure exerted by the very concentrated glucose solution will actually draw water out of the bloodstream and into the intestine. This results in a loss of available body water, effectively increasing dehydration.

6Very concentrated solutions of glucose (more than 6%) can have an adverse effect on fluid balance9

Although it has a chemical structure similar to glucose, the fruit sugar fructose diffuses passively across the intestinal wall. Studies have shown that fructose is absorbed more slowly than glucose and that it promotes less water uptake [19]. Moreover, fructose is known to exert a greater osmotic pressure, which means that, for a given concentration, it is more likely to draw water into the intestine, which can cause abdominal distress. These properties make fructose much less desirable as an energy component in sports drinks than glucose.

A study on cyclists compared the effects of glucose and fructose in a 6% solution during a 1hr 45min bout of cycling [20]. By comparison with glucose, fructose was associated with more gastrointestinal distress, a greater loss of plasma volume, higher levels of stress hormone and substantially poorer exercise performance!

Properly formulated carbohydrate/electrolyte drinks can and do increase hydration (and, as a bonus, supply extra carbohydrate to working muscles), so it's hardly surprising that they really do enhance performance when fluid loss is an issue [21-29]. But what's the best strategy for individual athletes? And how do you decide on the best drinks for you? Here are some simple guidelines derived from the evidence referred to in this article:

Pre-exercise

- Make sure your normal diet contains plenty of water and a minimum of other substances known to impair hydration;
- Drink ample (but not excessive) water in the run up to a training session or event;
- Consider using glycerol for hyper-hydration only if you are an elite athletes undertaking long endurance events in extremely hot conditions. Even then it has its drawbacks.

Post-exercise

- Follow Ron Maughan's advice on replacing lost fluid in terms of volume *(see page 67)*;
- Drinks containing electrolytes (especially sodium) stimulate the desire to drink and may therefore be preferable to plain water. There's also evidence that these drinks are absorbed more efficiently from the small intestine, especially when carbohydrate is present;
- Remember that you'll need to absorb extra fluid for glycogen replenishment – about 300ml for every 100g of carbohydrate consumed.

Mid-exercise

- For events lasting less than 30 minutes, mid-exercise fluid replacement isn't necessary, since it's not possible to lose enough fluid to affect performance in such a short time;
- Weather and exercise intensity affect fluid needs; the higher the temperature, humidity and exercise intensity, the greater the rate of fluid replacement required;
- Gastric emptying is most efficient when there is a high fluid volume in the stomach, so start exercise with fluid on board and drink little and often to keep it topped up;
- Gastric emptying is also affected by the concentration of a drink. The more concentrated the drink, the slower it empties;
- Plain water empties rapidly, as do low concentration (hypotonic) drinks and isotonic drinks. More recent research also suggests that energy drinks containing up to 4-5% glucose also empty as rapidly as water. However drinks

containing glucose and sodium are absorbed from the intestine more rapidly than plain water;

- More concentrated drinks (more than 6%) leave the stomach more slowly, but still manage to deliver more carbohydrate. Where energy replacement is the priority, these drinks are recommended, although they are less efficient for hydration;
- Where hydration is the priority, water, isotonic or low concentration glucose drinks will all suffice, though hypotonic/isotonic electrolyte/glucose containing drinks may be absorbed more rapidly from the intestine;
- Whatever sports drink you choose, ensure it contains electrolyte minerals;
- Where hydration is your goal, water is okay but high volumes of plain water are not recommended where profuse and prolonged sweating occurs (more than 3-4 litres lost) because of the risk of sodium dilution. If water is your preferred drink, consider using salt tablets in these circumstances;
- The evidence in favour of glucose polymer drinks is mixed. Overall, they may confer a slight advantage in terms of gastric emptying, but be prepared to pay more!
- Fructose or pure fruit juice drinks are not absorbed rapidly and may cause abdominal distress;
- Never experiment with a new drink during competition. Try it in training first to see how your body tolerates it!
- Choose a drink you find palatable. If it doesn't taste nice, you won't drink it, no matter how advanced the formula!

Andrew Hamilton

References

1. *Geigy Scientific Tables, 8th Ed, Ciba-Geigy Ltd 1981*

2. *Human Physiology, 2nd Ed, Springer-Verlag, Berlin. 1989*

3. *Appl Physiol 80:1112-1117, 1996*

4. *Int J Sports Nutr 7:104-116, 1997*

5. *Amer J Physiol 258 (Gastrointest. Liver Physiol.) 21: G216-G222, 1990*

6. *Medicine and Science in Sports and Exercise, 28:1260-1271, 1996*

7. *International Journal of Sports Nutrition, 15:329, 1997*

8. *Medicine and Science in Sports and Exercise 23, 307-313, 1990*

9. *Medicine and Science in Sports and Exercise, 23 314-319, 1990*

10. *J Physiol 154: 254-269, 1960*

11. *J Physiol 245: 209-225, 1975*

12 *Medicine and Science in Sports and Exercise, 24; S70, 1992*

13. *Gastroenterology 89: 1326-1330, 1985*

14. *Res Quart 51: 299-305, 1980*

15. *Eur J Appl Physiol Occup Physiol, 58(6): 605-12, 1989*

16. *Medicine and Science in Sports and Exercise, 18: 568-575, 1986*

17. *J Appl Physiol, 72(2): 468-75, 1992*

18. *J Pediatr, 106(3): 383-9, 1985*

19. *J Clin Invest, 55(4): 728-37, 1975*

20. *Medicine and Science in Sports and Exercise, 21:275-282, 1989*

21. *Medicine and Science in Sports and Exercise, 27:S223,1995*

22. *European Journal of Applied Physiology, 70:154-160, 1995*

23. *Medicine and Science in Sports and Exercise: Vol. 27, No. 2:200-210, 1995*

24. *American Journal of Clinical Nutrition, 48:1023-1033, 1988*

25. *Medicine and Science in Sports and Exercise, 20:110-115, 1988*

26. *Medicine & Science in Sports & Exercise, 31: S123, 1999*

27. *Journal of Applied Physiology, 71(6):2518-2527, 1991*

28. *American Journal of Physiology, 258:G216-G222, 1990*

29. *International Journal of Sports Medicine, 13:399-406, 1992*

How to calculate your personal fluid needs

Recently I have been engaged in fluid balance testing research with professional football clubs. This work has provoked much interest in the football world and carries some important lessons for athletes in other sports too. The key finding to emerge from it is that there is no standard answer to the following questions commonly asked by athletes:

- What is the best drink?
- How much of it should I consume?

Many factors will combine and interact to determine the answers to those questions. However, the answers will vary according to the nature of the event and the weather conditions at the time, so there is not even a standard answer for any given individual. It is important that athletes recognise this fact and stop searching for a single solution to all their needs.

Many expert committees have toiled long and hard over the questions, but none has as yet had the courage to admit that they cannot come up with an answer. This has led to the publication of numerous sets of guidelines that appear, at first sight, to provide answers.

The American College of Sports Medicine (ACSM), for example, has published guidelines for endurance athletes recommending that 'During exercise, athletes should start drinking early and at regular intervals in an attempt to consume fluids at a rate sufficient to replace all the water lost through sweating (*ie* body weight loss), or consume the maximal amount that can be tolerated'[1].

The ACSM also advises: 'During intense exercise lasting longer than 1h, it is recommended that carbohydrates be ingested at a rate of 30-60 [grams per hour] to maintain oxidation of carbohydrates and delay fatigue. This rate of carbohydrate intake can be achieved without compromising fluid delivery by drinking 600-1200 [ml per hour] of solutions containing 4%-8% carbohydrates (*ie* 40-80g per 100ml).'

The International Marathon Medical Directors Association (IMMDA) has recommended a fluid intake of something between 400 and 800 ml per hour, with the higher rates being appropriate for faster or heavier runners and the lower rates for slower runners and walkers [2].

The problem with both sets of recommendations is that they are too inflexible. The ACSM guidelines can be interpreted as encouraging runners to drink as much as they can: this may be more than is necessary and can lead to problems of water overload and even hyponatraemia (a potentially dangerous fall in the blood sodium level – see box on page 56). Even at the narrower range set by the IMMDA, 400 ml will not be enough for a heavy runner on a hot day, while 800 ml is likely to be too much for a light runner taking five hours to complete a marathon on a cold day.

6 The only sensible advice is for individual athletes to take personal responsibility for developing their own hydration plan 9

The only sensible advice is for individual athletes to take personal responsibility for developing their own hydration plan, and this is implied in the first ACSM recommendation, encouraging runners to drink just enough to replace fluid lost in sweat. That means looking at what you currently do, assessing that against what you should be doing and seeing if any changes need to be made. There are now many surveys of how much people drink in endurance races, and of how much these same people sweat.

If we look at what people actually do, we can use as an example a paper published by Tim Noakes and his colleagues in the *British Journal of Sports Medicine* last year [3]. They weighed 258 competitors before and after an Ironman distance triathlon held in South Africa in 2000 and 2001. Analysis of the results showed that weight change ranged from a loss of 8.0 kg (10.7% of the pre-race weight) to a gain of 3.0 kg (3.7%). In other words, some people finished the race severely dehydrated while others drank so much that they gained weight. There was no measure of how much fluid competitors consumed during the race, but we can guess that those who lost most weight probably drank a lot less than those who gained weight.

I and my colleagues have measured the fluid intakes of many top football players in training; it's a simple matter of weighing their drinks bottles before and after training, having made sure that they drink only from their own bottles – and that no-one else does! We saw that some players would put away almost two litres of fluid in a 90-minute training session while others drank almost nothing. They all did the same training and they all had access to the same drinks, so why this large difference?

At present, there are no good explanations for why some people sweat copiously while others hardly sweat at all. If you're a sweaty person, you just have to learn to cope with it. What we do tend to find, though, is that those who drink most are not necessarily those who sweat most; and this is consistent with the belief that thirst is not closely related to sweat loss – at least not when this amount is relatively small – and therefore not a reliable guide to fluid needs.

There is some evidence that the people who drink most are those who begin a training session already dehydrated: we don't yet know if this applies to a race situation, but it seems reasonable to suspect that it does.

The fact that fluid gains and losses could be measured in so many competitors in a race situation and in top professional footballers in training shows it's not hard to do. In fact, it can be achieved by anyone with access to a set of scales. Just weigh yourself before and after a long run and you'll have a good idea of whether you are a sweaty runner or not. Sweaty runners should probably be encouraged to drink more than their counterparts who merely 'glow' while exercising.

How much should you drink?
There has been a tendency to move away from the ACSM suggestion that everyone should aim to replace as much fluid as they lose in sweat with the aim of finishing the race weighing the same as when they started. There is probably no real danger to either performance or health from mild levels of

'There is probably no real danger to either performance or health from mild levels of dehydration'

dehydration. Yes, severe dehydration will certainly result in a loss of performance capacity, but a little dehydration means less weight to carry over those last few miles, and that may confer some benefits.

As a rule of thumb, during an endurance event you should aim to drink just enough to be sure you lose no more than about 1-3% of your pre-race weight. That may seem a difficult strategy to put in place, but all you need are a set of scales, some common sense and a sense of personal responsibility.

First, you need to record your body weight before and after as many of your long runs as you can. Weigh yourself at the last minute before going out, after that last-minute visit to the toilet. It is best to do this without any clothes, as even a vest and shorts can soak up a lot of sweat and make you seem heavier after the run than you really are.

Weigh yourself as soon as you get back again and note the two measurements in your training diary. (You do keep a training log, don't you? At any rate you should if you are at all serious about training.) You should also log the approximate distance and duration of the run, and perhaps also how you felt while running. Make a note, too, of whether you were wearing T-shirt and shorts or full tracksuit, hat and gloves.

If you have had anything to drink during the run, you need to know how much and add it to the amount of weight lost. Kitchen scales are perfectly good for weighing your drinks bottle. However, if you use a bottle with calibration marks on the side, you don't need to weigh it at all. You'll soon get the hang of this weighing and measuring, and once it is part of your routine it should be no inconvenience at all.

The sums are much easier to calculate if you work in kilograms and litres rather than pounds and pints, since 1kg of weight loss is roughly equal to one litre of sweat, while 1lb of weight loss is four fifths of a (standard British) pint. There are some errors in these calculations, as you will also be using up some stored fuels in the form of carbohydrate and fat, but these can be ignored with no great loss of accuracy.

Another thing to note is the weather conditions. Your local

paper will give you the temperature for the previous day, so you can look this up and add it to your other measurements. Ideally, you should also note the humidity (information available from your nearest weather station and on the Internet). How much effort you put into gathering this data will depends on how serious you are about going for that performance on race day.

After a few weeks, you should begin to see some patterns emerging. You will probably lose more weight (sweat) on longer runs, when you run faster, or when the weather is warmer or more humid. You can get rid of the first of these sources of variability by calculating your sweat rate per hour. This may be as little as 200-300ml or as much as 2-3 litres, depending on your physiology, your running speed, clothing and conditions. If you collect enough measurements, you should be able to allow for each of these factors and get an idea of how much you should be drinking in any given set of conditions.

Once you know what your sweat losses are likely to be in a particular set of conditions, you can plan for race day. You know the distance, you know how fast you plan to run and you have seen the weather forecast. That's all you need to know in order to plan your drinking strategy.

Two hypothetical examples

Let's take a look at how this might work in practice, using two different hypothetical examples:

1. You weigh 70 kg and you plan to run for three hours at a temperature of 20°C. You know that you sweat about 1 litre per hour at this pace and temperature, so you can expect to lose about three litres of sweat. Because you want to lose no more than about 2-3% of your body weight – that's 1.4-2.1 kg, or 1.4-2.1litres of fluid – you should aim to drink something between 900ml and 1.6 litres during the race. That's about 300-500 ml per hour, rather less than most of the recommendations suggest and probably a lot more comfortable.

2. You weigh 60 kg and plan to run 10 miles in about 62 minutes on a hot day (about 25°C). You will sweat about 2.2 litres in that hour. A 2-3% loss in body weight represents 1.2-1.8 litres

of fluid, so you should plan to drink about 400-1,000ml. This is a wide range, and you can probably opt for something near the lower end of it.

See, it's not really so difficult after all!

Ron Maughan

References

1. *http://www.acsm-msse.org/pt/pt-core/template-journal/msse/media/0196.htm*

2. *Clin J Sports Med 2003 Sep:309-18*

3. *Br J Sports Med 2004, 38; 718-724*

WHAT THE PAPERS SAY
Reports on recent acclimatisation-related studies by
Isabel Walker and Clare Whitehead

Technical clothing offers limited practical benefits

The so-called 'technical' athletic clothing fabrics, which purport to promote sweat evaporation from the skin, provide no thermoregulatory, physiological or comfort advantages when compared with traditional cotton clothing during or after exercise in a moderately warm environment.

This was the clear and somewhat surprising conclusion of a study on eight well-trained, well-hydrated men, carried out in the Human Performance Laboratory of Indiana University.

The researchers were investigating the hypothesis that: 'important physiological variables classically accepted to be affected by exercise in the heat (*ie* skin temperature, core temperature, heart rate and sweat loss) would show less perturbation with garments made from a fabric with improved evaporative characteristics as compared with ensembles of more traditional fabrics'.

Each subject carried out three identical submaximal treadmill tests wearing each of the following ensembles, plus running shoes:
- short-sleeved T-shirt, cycling shorts and anklet socks made from an evaporative polyester fabric;
- the same items of clothing made from a traditional cotton fabric;
- lycra swim suit and anklet socks (the 'semi-nude' condition).

Each trial consisted of 20 minutes of quiet seated rest in an environmental chamber, 30 minutes of treadmill running at 70% of VO_2max, 15minutes of treadmill walking at 40% of VO_2max and 15 minutes of seated rest. The chamber was heated to 30ºC, with a relative humidity of about 35. Wind speeds were applied to match the subjects' activity – *ie* highest during running and lowest during rest.

A variety of measurements – including clothing mass, body mass and body temperature – were taken before and after the trials. Key results were as follows:
- *Temperature.* There were no differences in any temperature variables between ensembles during running, walking and post-

exercise rest. In response to changes in exercise conditions, there were similar rates of change in body, rectal and skin temperature with all ensembles;

- *Metabolic requirements.* There were no differences in oxygen consumption or heart rate between ensembles at any point;
- *Comfort.* There were no differences in thermal comfort or sweating sensations between ensembles.
- However, there was a difference in the retention of sweat by the clothing ensembles, with the cotton outfit retaining approximately three times more sweat than either the synthetic or the semi-nude variants.

'It is therefore evident,' point out the researchers, 'that the synthetic material...does promote greater evaporation, as claimed by the manufacturer. In spite of this, the [cotton] ensemble did not impair temperature regulation in a warm environment.'

They acknowledge, though, that the same might not be true of cold environments 'where post-exercise evaporation may create a significant cooling effect, especially during intermittent exercise. Thus, the use of fabrics that promote evaporation may have a potentially greater benefit during exercise in a cold environment'.

This latter theory remains to be demonstrated. Meanwhile, the main message from the current study is that 'neither modest differences in the amount of clothing worn nor the fabric characteristics of the clothing alter physiological, thermoregulatory or comfort sensation responses during exercise in a moderately warn environment'.
Med Sci Sports Exerc 2001 Dec 33(12), pp2124-2130

Why heat's not such a bad thing

According to popular wisdom, heat exposure damages exercise performance, while lowering body temperature improves it. But this theory has been cast into doubt by a study which showed no difference in maximal exercise performance in healthy subjects exposed alternately to hot (35°C) and cold (15°C) conditions.

Eight physically active men performed three successive 15-minute rides on cycling ergometers at 30%, 50% and 70% of their peak sustained power output and then cycled at increasing work rates to exhaustion in both the hot and the cold environments, while researchers measured their skin and rectal (core) temperatures, heart rate and muscular activity.

Key results were as follows:

- There were no significant differences for maximal power output at exhaustion and time-to-exhaustion between the hot and cold rides;
- All skin temperatures were significantly higher throughout for hot than for cold and subjects felt more uncomfortable in the hot conditions. However, rectal temperatures were only slightly – and not significantly – higher;
- Heart rate was significantly higher in the hot group, but heart rate in both conditions increased similarly over time;
- There were no significant differences in muscle recruitment between the two conditions.

'Although the hot conditions increased heart rate and skin temperature,' comment the researchers, 'there were no differences in muscle recruitment or maximal performance, which suggests that the thermal stress of 35°C, in combination with exercise, did not impair maximal performance in this study.'

The key protective mechanism appears to have been the control of core temperature in the hot condition. For previous research has suggested that in hot conditions it is core temperature, rather than dehydration, energy production or metabolic rate changes, that is the critical factor limiting exercise capacity.

'It appears,' the researchers conclude, 'that under our hot conditions, effective peripheral thermoregulation mechanisms controlled core temperature, resulting in an unchanged neuromuscular recruitment strategy.'

Pflugers Arch 2002 Sep; 444(6), pp738-43

Precooling: do ice jackets work?

Precooling is seen as a useful way of preventing overheating during exercise and therefore enhancing performance – particularly for athletes who don't have time to acclimatise fully to hot environments before competition. And different methods of precooling – including cold water immersion, exposure to climate chambers and direct skin cooling – have been tried, with mixed results in terms of impact on performance.

Most recently, a team of Australian researchers have examined the effects of wearing ice cooling jackets on repeat sprint performance in warm and humid conditions – with results that can at best be described as disappointing.

After an initial familiarisation session, seven trained male hockey players performed two testing sessions, seven days apart, consisting of an 80-minute intermittent repeat sprint cycling exercise protocol inside a climate chamber set at 30°C and 60% relative humidity. For one of these sessions the subjects wore ice cooling jackets both before exercise (for five minutes) and during two five-minute and one 10-minute recovery periods. Measurements of performance (work done and power output on each sprint), heart rate, blood lactate concentration, core (rectal) and skin temperature, sweat loss, perceived exertion and ratings of thirst, thermal discomfort and fatigue were taken in both sessions.

Analysis of the results showed that chest skin temperature, thermal discomfort and rating of thirst were all significantly lower in the cooling condition. However, no significant differences were observed for measures of work performed, power output, heart rate, blood lactate concentrations, core or mean skin temperature, perceived exertion, sweat loss or ratings of fatigue.

In other words, although the athletes felt better in some ways when precooled, this increased comfort did not translate into enhanced performance.

Why did the ice jackets not do their job? The researchers believe this was because core temperature is the key variable where performance is concerned, and the cooling intervals used in this trial were simply not long enough to reduce core temperature to a significant extent.

Although the cooling intervals used were deliberately chosen to simulate realistic game-specific conditions for hockey and other sports requiring repeated high-intensity short sprints, the researchers suggest that further trials should be attempted, using longer exposure periods and additional cooling of the head and neck regions (with hoods or towels), before this method of precooling can be dismissed as useless.

Br J Sports Med 2003;37: pp 164-169

How to avoid heat cramps in tennis

Muscle cramps are an occupational hazard for athletes playing long tennis games in the heat. And a variety of so-called remedies have been prescribed, including trace minerals, amino acids, quinine, bananas and even pickle juice. But according to the US physician M F Bergeron, writing in the *Journal of Science and Medicine in Sport*, players can avoid debilitating heat cramps simply by being careful to replace salt and fluid losses.

Playing tennis in the heat presents a formidable challenge, even to the fittest players, he points out. And this is especially true when the heat is combined with high humidity. However, regular and copious water intake is often not enough to combat the effects of heat. Indeed excessive water intake can even be dangerous, increasing the risk of hyponatremia (sodium deficiency).

Adult and older adolescent tennis players generally lose up to 2.5 litres of sweat during each hour of competitive singles play in warm-to-hot environments, while fit, acclimatised players can lose even more. With a very high rate of sweating, players could easily incur a significant fluid deficit in long matches, even if they drink copious amounts on each changeover. And unless they can replace those losses rapidly, they risk starting the next match in a state of dehydration.

One potential outcome, according to Bergeron, is heat cramps, which often begin with 'twitches' in one or more voluntary muscles (such as the calves or quadriceps), particularly during a changeover period, and can progress rapidly to widespread debilitating muscle spasms that can leave affected players writhing in pain on court.

He recommends that at the first signs of muscle twitching, players can avoid progression by consuming an appropriate salt solution (eg 3g of salt dissolved in 16-20oz of Gatorade), drinking half on the current or next changeover and the rest on the one after that. Prevention is clearly a preferred option, though, and this can be achieved by boosting the salt content of the diet.

Bergeron offers the following tips for tennis players facing hot-weather competition:

- Arrive at tournament destinations as early as you can in order to acclimatise to the hot environment as thoroughly as possible;

- Drink plenty of fluids throughout the day, while being careful not to 'over-hydrate';
- If prone to heat cramps, add some salt to your diet and possibly add more salt to your on-court sports drink;
- Consider having sweat rate and sweat electrolyte losses measured so that specific strategies can be developed for maintaining your individual fluid and mineral balance;
- If heat cramps persist, consult your doctor about potential other causes, including medications, underlying illness or metabolic disorder.

Journal of Science and Medicine in Sport 6(1): pp 19-27

Sleep deprivation and performance

It may seem obvious to suggest that sleep deprivation has a deleterious effect on anaerobic performance – or, indeed, on performance of any kind. But did you know that performance is more likely to be impaired in the evening than the morning?

That, in any case, is the key finding of a French study, set up to investigate the impact of one sleepless night on performance of brief, high-intensity exercise at different times of the day.

Reduced performance following sleep disturbance could be caused by a disruption to the body's circadian rhythms – physiological variables that fluctuate over the course of a 24-hour period. These rhythmic changes, including body temperature and levels of arousal, tend to drop during the night and peak in the afternoon, and are linked to better performance in the early evening than the morning.

In the French study, a group of 13 male subjects performed two 30-second power test sessions on a cycle ergometer after 24 and 36 hours without sleep (at 6am and 6pm). For purposes of comparison, they also performed the same tests at the same time after a good night's sleep.

As expected, peak, mean and maximal power production were higher at 6pm than at 6am, irrespective of the previous night's sleep pattern, suggesting the overriding influence of a circadian rhythm. However, there was a reduction of time-of-day effect after a sleepless night, such that evening performance was impaired although morning performance was unchanged.

Impaired performance of brief high-intensity exercise after 36 hours of sleep loss has not been demonstrated in previous studies, and the French researchers offer the following possible explanations for their findings:

- Power production may itself follow a rhythmic cycle that is affected by sleep deprivation;
- A change in the circadian rhythm of arousal, caused by sleep deprivation, may have resulted in reduced levels of motivation in the evening;

Body temperature measurements, taken orally every two hours, showed a circadian rhythm in both situations, with temperatures minimal at 6am and maximal at around 6pm. Such changes in body temperature could be linked to the observed improvement in evening performance, perhaps due to a similar effect seen after warming up, which elevates muscle temperature, increasing the rate of metabolic reactions and nerve signalling and reducing muscle viscosity. Sleep loss resulted in a slight phase advancement in body temperature, such that peak temperature no longer coincided with the evening test session.

These findings reinforce the need for a good night's sleep before anaerobic competition – particularly where morning heats are followed by finals in the late afternoon. Where relevant, travel plans should be adjusted to allow for time to overcome jet lag, and relaxation techniques employed to reduce the risk of pre-competition sleeplessness.

European Journal of Applied Physiology, 2003, 89:359-366

How time zone travel harms performance

New evidence for a deleterious effect of air travel on sporting performance has come from an Australian study analysing its effects during six seasons of the Australian National Netball Competition.

Archival data from those seasons (1997-2002) were analysed, with comparisons made between 'pairs' of games in which teams played each other both at home and away during the same season.

The aim of the study was to assess the influence of travel within and across time zones on netball team performance. Pairs of games were grouped according to the travel required to reach the opponent's court, as follows:

1. Local (LT) – less than one hour's travel;
2. North or south travel (NS) without a time zone shift;
3. East or west travel with a time zone shift of less than two hours (EW1);
4. East or west travel with a two-hour time zone shift (EW2).

The change in performance with travel was assessed by comparing the points difference for each pair of games for each of the four groups; *ie* if team A defeated team B by 10 points at home but by only five points away, the points difference (travel cost) would be five points.

Analysis revealed that travel across a two-hour time zone (EW2) was the only condition in which there was a significant difference between points scored at home and away.

'These results suggest,' comment the researchers, 'that relatively brief air travel... can influence team performance'. This finding provides some support for the 'circadian dysrhythmia hypothesis' (*aka* jet lag), but other factors could include the well-established 'home-ground advantage' and the process of travel itself.

J Sci Med Sport 2004;7:1, pp118-122

Notes